Safari

Gail Tuchman

SCHOLASTIC INC.
New York Toronto London Auckland
Sydney Mexico City New Delhi Hong Kong

For Lauren—with love on your "journey."
—G.T.

ISBN 978-0-545-34266-7

12 11 10 9 8 7 6 5 4 3   11 12 13 14 15 16/0

Printed in the U.S.A.   40

First Scholastic printing, February 2011

cover, Beverly Joubert/ NationalGeographicStock.com; 1, Panoramic Images/ Getty Images; 2, Eric Isselée/ Shutterstock; 3, Remi Benali/ Corbis; 4-5, Remi Benali/Corbis; 6, WorldFoto/ Alamy/ Alamy; 11, Dave Hamman/ Gallo Images/ Getty Images; 8-9, Karine Aigner/ NationalGeographicStock.com; 12, Mitsuaki Iwago/ Minden Pictures/ NationalGeographicStock.com; 13 top, James Warwick/ The Image Bank/ Getty Images; 13 bottom left, D7INAMI7S/ Shutterstock; 13 bottom right, Michael Nichols/ NationalGeographicStock.com; 14-15, Panoramic Images/ Getty Images; 16, Bobby Model/ NationalGeographicStock.com; 19, Mitsuaki Iwago/ Minden Pictures; 20 top right, ZSSD/ Minden Pictures; 20 bottom left, D7INAMI7S/ Shutterstock; 20 bottom right, Mitsuaki Iwago/ NationalGeographicStock.com; 20 top right, Suzi Eszterhas/ Minden Pictures; 21 right, Kletr/ Shutterstock; 22-23, Matrin Harvey/ Foto Natura/ Minden Pictures/ NationalGeographicStock.com; 24, Norbert Rosing/ NationalGeographicStock.com; 21 left, George F. Mobley/ NationalGeographicStock.com; Hippo illustrations by Dan Sipple.

Hello! **Jambo!**
Let's go.

I'm going on safari.

What will I see?

I see elephants spray,
just for me.

I see elephants spray,
on safari.

I see lions play,
just for me.

I see lions play,
on safari.

I see rhinos run,
just for me.

I see rhinos run,
on safari.

Rhinos run.
Lions play.
Elephants spray.

What else will
I see on safari?

I see giraffes eat,
just for me.

I see giraffes eat,
on safari.

I see zebras graze,
just for me.

I see zebras graze,
on safari.

I see hippos soak,
just for me.

I see hippos soak,
on safari.

Hippos soak.
Zebras graze.
Giraffes eat.
Rhinos run.
Lions play.
Elephants spray.

What else will I see?

I see animals all around me...

on safari!